W9-DGH-809

Tales from Count Lucanor

TALES FROM COUNT LUCANOR

by Don Juan Manuel · adapted from the Spanish by

Toby Talbot · woodcuts by Rocco Negri

THE DIAL PRESS / NEW YORK

For Don Daniel

Contents

Prologue / *Just as men's faces vary, so do their minds and wills.*

And to show you this, I, Don Juan, son of the Infante Don Manuel, have written these examples. Since people do not take pleasure in reading difficult books I have tried to use the simplest and most pleasing words I could find. I hope my readers will be enlightened and amused and that the good advice in the book will not be lost.

Tales from Count Lucanor

About a Young Man Who Married a Wild and High-Strung Wife

One day Count Lucanor called his adviser Patronio to him and said, "One of my servants is courting a wealthy young woman whose family is richer than his own. A marriage would be most desirable, except for one thing. The young woman has a violent and impetuous temper. What advice should I give to my servant?"

And Patronio replied, "Well, if the servant is at all like the son of a man I knew, let the marriage take place, by all means. But if he is not, forbid it."

The Count begged for an explanation, and Patronio related this story.

"Once there lived in a certain village a good man who had a son, the most promising youth in the world. But the lad was not rich enough to accomplish the deeds which in his heart he felt equal to. Hence he was unhappy, because he had the will but not the power to pursue his goals.

"Now their neighbor was a much richer man, and one with a higher position. He had an only daughter who was the very opposite of the young man. For while he always behaved in the most civilized way, she was as wild as could be and given to utter contrariness. There wasn't a man alive who cared to marry such a little devil.

"One day, the young man went to his father and said, 'Since I do not possess enough money for either myself or a wife to live comfortably, I must either abandon my native land and seek my fortune elsewhere, or make an advantageous marriage.'

"The father thought his son's ideas seemed sound, and he encouraged him to seek a proper marriage.

"Then the youth suggested that if his father agreed he would ask for the hand of their wealthy neighbor's daughter. When he heard this proposal, the man threw his hands to his head and cried out, 'How can you even dream of such a thing?'

"But the son insisted and pleaded for so long that in the end the father gave his consent and agreed to go to his neighbor, the father of the perverse wench, though the idea to him was sheer folly. Since the two men were very good friends, the young man's father freely told his neighbor of his son's wish. When the townsman heard the proposal, he exclaimed: 'By heaven, if I did that, I would truly be a false friend, for you have a fine son, and it would be wicked of me to consent to something that would end either in his injury or his death. I feel certain that if he marries my daughter, he will soon die or at least, prefer death to life. Now pray, do not think I say this out of any objection to the alliance. In fact, I would be grateful to any man who would take that girl out of my house.'

"The young man's father was overjoyed to hear this and thanked him.

"So the wedding was held and the bride taken to her husband's home.

"Now it is an old Moorish custom after a wedding to prepare supper for the newlyweds and then leave them alone until the following day. And that is what was done. But both the young man's parents as well as the bride's parents returned to their own homes with great misgivings, for they felt sure that they would find the bridegroom either dead or gravely injured.

"As soon as the newlyweds were alone in the house, they sat down to table for supper. Before the bride could open her mouth, the bridegroom spotted his dog wandering about the room. He shouted: 'Dog, bring me water to wash my hands!'

Naturally the dog made no move to do so. Ferociously the young man repeated his order. Again the canine did not obey. The youth rose in a rage, unsheathed his sword, and fell upon the poor animal. The frightened creature fled, bounding from one spot to another, the young man behind him, lunging over the table, in and around chairs, over the fireplace . . . until finally he caught the dog with his sword. He pierced him through, hacked away at him, and hewed off his head, leaving a trail of blood behind.

"Thus, bloodstained and full of wrath, he again sat down at the table. After a while he spied the cat: 'Bring me water for my hands,' he raved to the animal. The cat, too, did not move, and the young man cried out: 'What, you impudent scoundrel! Did you not see how I treated the dog for daring to disobey me? Let me assure you that if you do not do as I tell you this instant, you will share his fate.'

"The cat did not heed him, since he, like the dog, was not in the habit of bringing water to anyone.

"Whereupon the young man leaped up, seized the poor animal by the paws, and flung him against the wall, displaying greater rage than he had with the dog.

"Muttering under his breath, his fury mounting, he again

placed himself at the table. Acting like a man possessed, his eyes darted about as if looking for something to attack next.

"His wife looked at him, convinced beyond doubt that he had lost his senses. But she said absolutely nothing.

"At length he set his eyes on his horse, the only one he owned, and arrogantly commanded the animal to bring him water. The young man bellowed: 'What, Master Horse? Think you that because you are the only horse I have you will get mercy if you dare to disobey me? Beware! Because if you do not carry out my command, I vow that you will not escape my vengeance. There is no creature in this world who refuses to obey me who is not treated the same as all others.'

"The horse did not move, and the man charged forward with sword in hand, killed, and beheaded him.

"When the poor bride saw that her husband had just killed his only horse (a Moor's greatest treasure), she realized that this was no game, and she was so frightened that she did not know if she were dead or alive.

"He again sat down at the table, raging and all bloody as he was, bellowing and swearing that if he had a thousand horses, or even men and women in the house who disobeyed him, he would kill them all.

"He kept looking around from one side of the table to the other, never abandoning his bloody sword. And since there was no other animal around, his glaring eyes fell on his wife: 'Get up, woman, and fetch me water for my hands.' She did not wait to be told a second time. Directly, she arose and gave him the water he asked for.

" 'Ah!' exclaimed her husband on seeing it. 'How thankful I am that you've obeyed me. Otherwise, irritated as I am by those senseless brutes, I would have done the very same to you.'

"And at once he ordered her to bring him his food. And she did. So stormy was he in tone and in manner that his wife thought at any moment her head would be rolling on the ground.

"Finally bedtime arrived. After allowing her to sleep for a short time, he bade her: 'Get up. I have been so annoyed that I cannot sleep. Be sure tomorrow that nothing disturbs me and make something nice for me to eat for breakfast.'

"While it was yet early the following morning, the fathers, mothers, and other relatives came stealthily to the door of the young couple's home. They were trembling. Since they heard no voices, they feared the young bridegroom was either dead or wounded. When they peered through the chinks of the door and saw only the bride, they no longer had any doubts.

"As soon as the bride saw her parents, she cautiously hastened to the door and implored them: 'Traitors, what do you think you're doing? How dare you approach this gate, even to chat? Hush! For if you don't we shall all be dead!'

"And from that day on the wild woman became docile and obedient, and the marriage enjoyed peace and blessed happiness.

"Now it happened a few days later that the bride's father tried to follow the example of his son-in-law in order to terrify his own wife, who was an ill-tempered crone. Pretending the utmost fury he took out his sword and killed a horse. But his wife only said, 'My dear, it is too late. It wouldn't help if you slayed a hundred horses. Those are things that must be done earlier. We know each other too well by now.'"

"Thus," said Patronio, "if your servant is the same as the young man in the story, let him by all means marry. But if he is not, he had better not take such a step."

The Count agreed that this advice made good sense, and he followed it.

The Fox Who
Pretended To Be Dead

Count Lucanor summoned his counselor: "Patronio, a relative of mine in a distant land cannot defend himself against his more powerful neighbor who harasses him continuously. He is now at his wit's end and prepared to defend himself rather than suffer more abuse. What can he do?"

"My Lord," said Patronio, "before advising you, I'd like to tell you what happened to a fox who pretended to be dead."

"One night a fox entered a henhouse. After killing many fowls he suddenly realized it was time to seek cover. But it was already daylight and people were moving about in the village. Seeing that he was unable to hide, he stealthily went into the street and stretched out as if he were dead.

"When the townsfolk saw him lying there, apparently dead, they paid him no heed.

"After a while a man passed by and remarked, 'The hairs from

a fox's forehead are an excellent remedy for temper tantrums in children.' So taking out his scissors, he clipped some hairs from the fox's brow.

"Soon another man came by and observed: 'The fur from the back and loins of a fox cures all sorts of complaints.' And so it went until the fox remained nearly shorn. Still he never moved for he knew that eventually his hair would grow back.

"And then along came someone else and declared: 'The nails of a fox's foot are a sure remedy for sudden fear, and he tore the nails out. Still the fox did not stir.

"At last another man approached and said, 'The heart of a fox works miracles for toothaches,' and he took out his knife ready to cut out the fox's heart.

"Now, when the fox realized that his heart was about to be removed and that he had no way of getting a new one, he decided to act. In a wink he sprang to his feet, bolted for shelter, and thus saved his skin."

"And you, Count Lucanor, advise your relative to ignore slight annoyances and let them pass. A man need not be ashamed because he is not as strong as his neighbor. But if his life or honor is in peril, bid him to act."

The Owls and the Crow

One day Count Lucanor was talking to Patronio, his adviser, "Patronio, there is a man of considerable influence with whom I don't get along. Now this man has a servant in his house, who is a relative of his and to whom he has been very kind. The other day the servant came to me, claiming that he had been ill-fed and ill-treated by his master, and offered me his services if I would show him how he could be revenged. Since I have such confidence in your advice, I wish you would tell me what to do."

"My Lord," Patronio began, "the first thing I can tell you is that this man may have come to deceive you. Please listen to what happened to the owls and the crows."

"The crows and the owls had a great conflict, and the crows were getting the worst of it. For since it is the owls' custom to come out at night and then by day to hide themselves in hard-to-find caves, each night they would fly to the trees where the crows nested and slay many of them.

"Beset by such slaughter from their enemies, the crows consulted the wisest and oldest crow of their lot. The wise old crow suggested a plan of revenge to them. And this is how it went.

"He had them pluck out all his feathers except for a few on his wings so that he would still be able to fly a little. In this sad state he went to the owls: 'See how cruelly the crows have treated me', he bemoaned, 'and simply because I tried to make peace between you. To avenge myself, I will show you many ways to besiege them.'

"When the owls heard this, they hooted with delight. They began to shower the crow with affection and to treat him splendidly. And they told him all their secrets and plans.

"Now among the owls there was one experienced, aged owl. As soon as he set eyes on the crow, he guessed the scheme.

"He hurried to the leader of the owls and advised him: 'This crow can only do us harm. He has come to spy on us. Let's kick him out!'

"But no one would believe the old owl. Seeing this, he wandered off alone to find a new hiding-place for himself.

"Meanwhile the crow continued to dwell amid the owls, gaining all their confidence. When his feathers were sufficiently grown to enable him to take a long flight, the crow told the owls: 'Since I can now fly with ease, I wish to go and see exactly where the crows are now. I shall then return to fetch you so that you can follow me and destroy them all.'

"The owls praised this idea.

"But when the crow returned he was not alone. Accompanying him were all the other crows whom he had informed of the owls' plans and hiding-places.

"The owls were thus attacked unprepared and in daylight were easy victims to the vengeance of the crows.

"Now this ill fortune befell the owls because they foolishly trusted the crow, their natural enemy."

"And you, Count Lucanor, beware of this man who has come to you. Since he is a member of your enemy's household, he is naturally interested in its welfare. I advise you therefore under no condition to place your confidence in him. If you do employ him let it be in a position which requires no trust. Otherwise, he may play you foul."

The Count followed this advice.

The King Who
Tried To Please His Wife

Count Lucanor and Patronio were chatting.

"Patronio, a man I know comes to me again and again, begging for help. Each time I grant it, he is grateful. But the other day he called on me again for aid, and this time when I could not do as he required, he grew angry and showed that he had forgotten his earlier debts. Pray, advise me what to do."

"My Lord," answered Patronio, "this reminds me of what happened to Ben Abit of Seville with Queen Ramaiquia, his wife.

"King Abit loved Ramaiquia more dearly than anyone else in the world. She was a very virtuous woman, and the Moors often recounted her many pious acts. But she had one grave fault. At times she was overcome by strange whims which the king was always willing to gratify.

"It happened that one day in February while they were visiting in the north it began to snow heavily. When Ramaiquia saw the snow, she started to cry as if in the deepest despair.

"The king asked, 'Why do you weep?'

" 'I weep because it never snows in our own land.'

"The king, anxious to please her, ordered almond trees to be planted upon all the mountains surrounding Cordoba, for that is a warm region and it hardly ever snows there. Now once a year, in February, the almond trees come forth in full blossom and the white flowering slopes appear as if they are covered with snow. This was a source of delight to the queen for a time.

"On another occasion while Ramaiquia was in her chamber peering out of her window, she saw on the banks of the river a barefoot woman kneading mud to make bricks. When Ramaiquia saw this, she promptly took to weeping. The king noticed this and beseeched her, 'Why do you weep so?'

" 'I'm never free to do what I please. I cannot do what yonder woman is doing,' she fretted.

"To gratify his wife, the king ordered the lake in Cordoba to be filled with rose water. To produce mud, he commanded sugar, cinnamon, lavender, cloves, amber, and other fragrant spices and perfumes to be strewn upon it. And in place of the straw sugar cane was sown.

"When this was done, he informed Ramaiquia, 'Now, my

dear, take off your shoes, enter the mud, and make all the adobe your heart desires.

"Some days later, taking a fancy for some other strange thing, the queen started crying once more. Again the king begged to know what ailed her.

"And she lamented, 'How can I refrain from tears, when you never do anything to please me?'

"Whereupon the king, realizing that he had done his utmost to gratify her caprices and feeling at his wits 'end, exclaimed in Arabic, *'Vâ la mahah el-tin,'* which means, 'And what about the day of the mud?' as if to say, 'If you have forgotten about all the rest, at least do not forget about the mud, which I prepared to humor you.' "

"And you, Count Lucanor, if you have done so much for this man and to no avail, I urge you to trouble yourself no more over him, lest he bring you harm. And, may I bid you also, never forget a good turn done you."

The advice pleased the Count, so he acted upon it, and the outcome was a happy one.

Once a Miser Crossed a River

One day the Count told Patronio: "I must travel to a distant part of the country in order to receive a large sum of money which I could employ most advantageously in my affairs. But I am fearful that in my return voyage I may be exposed to much danger. Please advise me what to do."

"My Lord," said Patronio, "listen to what happened to a man who had to cross a river while carrying a treasure."

"Gladly," the Count replied.

"This man," said Patronio, "who was toting a heavy bundle of precious stones came to a wide, muddy river. Since there was neither bridge nor boat, he had to walk through the water. So, carrying his shoes, he waded in. But he found that the weight of his shoes and that of the treasure loaded him down and made it difficult to avoid sinking. The mud became worse as he reached the deep part of the river.

"A man who stood on the opposite bank began to shout to him: 'Throw away your load, or you'll be lost!'

"But the foolish miser, never thinking that if he sank he would lose not only his treasure but his own life as well, would not heed the advice.

"The current was very strong, and as the mud became deeper the man gradually sank until the water reached his neck. He tried to free his feet from the mud but, alas, found it impossible.

"And so with the weight he carried, he rolled over and drowned in the river."

"As for you, Count Lucanor, you must decide whether the profits in view place your life in peril. If so I beseech you not to undertake your trip."

The Count agreed with this advice and promptly followed it.

The King and His Favorite

Once Count Lucanor was conversing with Patronio, and he said to him: "Patronio, the most curious thing has happened. A friend of mine, a powerful and respected nobleman, confided to me that he is planning to leave this country never to return. Out of his great regard for me, he wishes to leave me all of his land. Now this, of course, is a great honor and very tempting. But still I would like to hear your opinion and advice on the matter."

"Count Lucanor," said Patronio, "your own good sense needs little counsel from me. But since you desire my opinion, let me caution you against being deceived. In fact, your situation reminds me of what happened to a king and his favorite."

Count Lucanor begged Patronio to tell him the story.

"There was a king who had a most trusted minister. Eventually the sovereign's confidence and attachment to the favorite aroused the envy of others in the court, and they used every opportunity to speak evil of the minister to the king. The king, however, closed his ears to any suspicion or doubt about his favorite's loyalty.

"The jealous courtiers continued to nag the sovereign, and finally one day they came up with the story that the favorite was plotting the king's death and scheming to seize the crown and kingdom.

"So grave was this accusation that the king was now obliged to test its truth.

"The enemies of the favorite, noting the king's anxiety, coaxed their ruler into employing an ingenious ruse to prove the truth of what they said.

"And so several days later while the king was discussing other matters with his favorite, he happened to mention that he found himself growing disgusted with worldly affairs, and could find only vanity in them.

"Sometime afterward while talking with the favorite again, the king chanced to remark that his dislike for court life and manners was mounting daily. So often did the king repeat these sentiments in the days that followed that at last his favorite was convinced that the king truly took no pleasure in the honors, riches, or pleasures of his life.

"When the king felt quite certain that his favorite believed him he announced to him one day that he wished to retire from court. He would go to some secluded village where no one knew him and where he could enjoy peace and retirement.

"The favorite was aghast when he heard this and used every argument to dissuade his king.

"'You cannot,' he insisted, 'abandon the government of your country. It would be torn by strife and revolution. Your people would suffer. But even if the interests and peace of your subjects cannot sway you, you must weigh a more personal consideration. How can you leave your queen and your son exposed to such danger?'

"The king had his reply prepared: 'I have given much thought to this matter. In order to leave my queen and son protected, I shall entrust them to someone who is loyal and who enjoys all my confidence. That person is you. Furthermore, I shall leave you in command of all the country's fortresses, so that if, by chance, I never return to this land, or die far away from it, you will take charge of the prince's rearing and well-being until he comes of age and is able to rule the kingdom himself.'

"The minister was flattered and overwhelmed by the king's proposal, not only because of the confidence it implied, but also because of the great power that would come into his hands.

"Now in the favorite's home there lived a wise captive, a Moorish philosopher, whom he consulted on all important matters. As soon as the minister left the monarch, he hastened to the captive and, unable to conceal his pride in possibly having the whole kingdom under his sway, he recounted what had happened. But the captive philosopher quickly guessed the trap behind the king's proposal and counseled the now frightened man on how to escape the peril he was in.

"That very night the king's favorite shaved off his hair and beard. At the break of day he dressed himself in the rags, torn old shoes, and staff of a wandering beggar. He filled the lining of his garment with gold coins.

"He then appeared at the gate of the king's palace and told the gateman: 'Inform His Majesty in secret that I am here, waiting to depart with him and share his destiny before the people are awake!'

"The gateman was struck dumb with wonder to see the most distinguished of all the courtiers in this garb, but he obeyed the request and ran to inform his sovereign.

"Naturally, the king was astounded and told the gateman to admit his favorite.

"Once the favorite was in his presence, the monarch asked him, 'What are you doing in this strange style of dress?'

"The favorite replied, 'Since it is your plan to leave our country, I have decided to accompany you. No amount of persuasion can alter my resolution. All the honor and wealth I have I owe to you, and if you are determined to leave your queen, son, and kingdom, I shall travel with you and serve you with unceasing fidelity. I have assumed this dress so that we may travel unrecognized. In my clothes I have hidden enough gold to sustain us for the rest of our lives. But I suggest that we depart at once before our intentions are known.'

"When the king heard these words, he thanked his favorite with all his heart for this proof of loyalty. He then related to him how he had been deceived by evil tongues and had used this device to test his favorite's sincerity."

"Let me caution you, Count Lucanor, to beware of your friend's offer. He may be testing your feelings to find out if you are interested in his power and possessions. Assure him that you covet neither, for without confidence, friendship cannot long endure."

The Moorish King
and His Three Sons

One day Count Lucanor said to his adviser: "Patronio, many young men are being brought up in my court. Some are of noble birth, others are not. Now I find their manner and behavior so varied that I am at a loss to know which promises to turn into the worthiest. Can you advise me?"

"My Lord," said Patronio, "as far as the future goes, nothing is certain, especially when you're dealing with human beings. Often their outward traits are deceptive.

"But to judge which of the young men of your court will become the worthiest, I'd like to recall a tale about a Moorish king who tried to test which of his three sons would become the bravest."

"Tell me, Patronio, what he did."

"Well," Patronio began, "the father had to decide which of his sons should rule after he was too old to do so. The leading men of his kingdom were eager for him to name his successor. And the king promised that he would let them know his decision in one month.

"One afternoon about a week later, he beckoned his eldest son: 'I shall go riding early tomorrow morning, and I wish you to accompany me.'

"The next day the oldest son came to his father, but not as early as instructed. When he arrived, the king told him, 'I want to dress now. Please fetch my clothes.'

"Off went the son to the king's attendant and ordered: 'Bring the king his clothes.'

"The attendant asked, 'Which suit does His Majesty desire?'

"The son returned to his father and inquired, 'Which suit do you want?'

"The king replied, 'My state robe.'

"The young man went and informed the attendant: 'Bring his state robe.'

"Then the attendant asked, 'Which cape does the king wish?'

" 'My velvet one,' answered the king. And it was brought.

"This happened with every article of the king's attire, the son going back and forth, carrying questions and answers, until the king at last had all his garments. Then the attendant came

and dressed the king and helped him on with his boots.

"When he was dressed, the king bade his son: 'Fetch me my horse.'

"The son betook himself to the royal stable boy and commanded: 'Bring the king his horse.'

"'Which horse shall I bring?' asked the stable boy.

"The son returned to the king, 'Which horse shall he bring?'

"And for every little thing the king needed to mount his horse—saddle, bridle, spurs, sword, and so forth—the son went to and fro.

"When all was finally prepared, the king changed his mind and said, 'I have decided not to ride out. I wish you, my son, to go through the city in my stead, carefully observing everything worthy of notice, and on your return, come to me and give me your opinion of what you have seen.'

"The prince set out, accompanied by the king's most trusted men. Trumpets and cymbals and other musical instruments preceded this brilliant procession. After the son had ridden for a stretch through the city he returned to the palace.

"The king asked, 'What do you think of what you have seen?'

"His son replied, 'Nothing in particular, but I must say the cymbals and trumpets make a racket!'

"After a few days the king sent for his middle son to appear before him early in the morning. The king put this lad through the same test which he had used on the older brother. The youth reacted in a similar way and he too said that all was well in the kingdom.

"Some time later, the king ordered his youngest son to come before him at the break of day. Now this young man rose long before dawn and waited patiently until the king awoke. Then the boy entered and bowed before his father. The king bade him to fetch his clothes. The young prince asked his father to specify what he wished to wear and then brought him everything at once. He refused to allow the attendant to help him, insisting on doing it all himself and said to the king, 'If you permit me, Father, I would be honored to wait on you.'

"When the king was dressed, he requested his son to bring his horse. Again the son asked which horse, saddle, spurs, and sword his father desired, as well as everything else needed for riding. He then brought everything without any further questions.

"When all was ready, the king as before declared, 'Today I shall not go out, but I want you to go, and on your return, relate to me what you think worthy of notice.'

"The youngest son set out, escorted by the same courtiers as his older brothers. As the prince rode on, he asked his escort to show him the interior of the city, the streets where the king guarded his treasures, the mosques, the sections where the nobility lived and where the commoners dwelt. Then he summoned all the soldiers for inspection, both cavalry and infantry, and ordered them to perform their maneuvers and display their weapons. Next he visited the walls of the city, the towers and the fortresses. When this was done, it was very late. He returned to the palace.

"'Well,' said the king, 'what have you seen?'

"The young prince replied, 'I fear giving offense, Father. But if you think it will not upset you, I shall tell you what I saw.'

"'If you desire my blessing, hold nothing back.'

"'Though I am sure you are a good king, I do not think you have done as much as you might, having such good troops, so much power, and such great resources. Many of your subjects live poorly and the government is mismanaged. Yet if you so desired, you might have made this the greatest country in the world.'

"The king was overjoyed at hearing this sensible judgment.

"When the time came for him to announce his decision to the

people of the land, he proclaimed: 'Your next king will be my youngest son. Though I would have liked to appoint my eldest to govern, I feel it my duty to select the one who has shown himself most fit!' "

"And, Count Lucanor, if you desire to know which of the young men in your court is the most promising, try by similar means to examine their qualities."

The Count praised Patronio for this advice.

About a Man Who
Had Nothing To Eat but Peas

"Patronio," said Count Lucanor, "I realize that God has been bountiful with me, granting me more than I can individually enjoy, but although my affairs go well and honorably, I sometimes feel so pressed for money that life is a burden to me. Pray counsel me."

"My Lord," said Patronio, "allow me to recount what happened to two rich men."

"One of these men fell upon such hard times that he no longer had anything to eat. Weak from hunger he went begging from door to door until weary, but was given nothing to eat except a handful of dried peas. When he recalled how rich he had been the man began to cry bitterly. Since he was starving, however, he ate the peas, but continued to weep as he tossed the empty pods behind him.

"Suddenly he noticed a man following him, who was collecting

and eating the discarded pods. 'Why,' he asked, 'are you eating those pods?'

" 'Because,' said the other, 'though I was once much richer than you, I am now so poor and hungry that I am glad to eat the pods you are throwing away.'

"Hearing this the first man felt some consolation, knowing that there was someone poorer than himself, and even less deserving of his lot.

"He plucked up courage, worked hard, and prospered ever after."

"And you, My Lord, must know that in this world, no man has everything. If your life is honorable and your circumstances decent, do not worry if at times you are pressed for funds. Think of others of even nobler rank and greater fortune who are in tighter straits."

Encouraged by Patronio's tale, Count Lucanor faced his predicament and soon solved it.

Who Will Toll the Morning Bells?

"Patronio," said Count Lucanor, "a friend and I agreed to a venture which would benefit both of us. The time to act has now come, but he is out of town at the moment and I don't dare to do anything until his return. Pray advise me in this."

"My Lord," replied Patronio, "may I tell you of a similar situation which arose among the canons of the Cathedral of Paris and a convent of friars?"

"Please do," the Count urged.

"Once upon a time the canons of the cathedral decided that since they were the superior order in the church they had the right to toll the first morning bells.

"The friars disagreed with this claim. They argued, 'Since we are obliged to rise very early to study and sing our morning chants, we should toll the first bell and wait for no one, including canons.

"The argument turned into a costly lawsuit, because neither party was willing to give in. And the only ones to benefit from the situation were the lawyers.

"Time passed and still the lawsuit was not resolved. Finally a mandate from the Pope arrived, referring the dispute to a cardinal. When the cardinal arrived in Paris to settle the matter he commanded all the documents of the prolonged case to be brought before him.

"Despite the imposing array of legal seals and papers, the cardinal, an astute man, summoned the canons and friars to appear before him on the following day. It seemed impossible for any man to read, understand, and pass a verdict on such a complicated and drawn-out dispute. But since he was the Pope's emissary both parties felt compelled to obey.

"The next day friars and canons assembled before the cardinal. The meeting promised to be a solemn one. 'My friends,' began the cardinal, 'this case has gone on long enough, costing both parties time, trouble, and money. First of all, I say, this tower of paper must be burned.'

"Then he paused, and to the great astonishment of all, he passed the following decision: 'The first ones to rise shall toll the morning bells!' "

"And you, Count Lucanor, if the project you are considering is advantageous to both you and your friend, and if you are able to get on with it alone, I advise you not to waste time. Good opportunities are often lost through hesitation and delay."

The Count was delighted by this advice and acted upon it.

A Note About *Count Lucanor*

Don Juan Manuel, a prince born in the year 1281, was the nephew of King Alfonso the Learned. In his extremely active lifetime he engaged in both politics and literature. He served as Regent of Castile for Alfonso XI, fought against the Moors, who still occupied part of Spain, and yet managed from time to time to retire to his castles and estates, where he wrote fourteen books, eight of which are preserved. He was that ideal man of Spain's subsequent Golden Age of the sixteenth and seventeenth centuries: a man of arms and a man of letters.

His masterpiece, *The Book of the Examples of Count Lucanor and Patronio,* or as it is more simply known, *Count Lucanor,* was completed in 1335, over a decade before Boccaccio's *Decameron,* with which it is often compared. It is a collection of fifty exemplary or moral tales and fables strung together within one framework.

Count Lucanor, a young nobleman beset with many problems of life and government, asks the advice of his old counselor, Patronio, who each time relates a pertinent story. Each example or tale is then summed up with its moral. In this collection, whose aim is to reveal Don Juan as a master story-teller rather than a didactician, the concluding morals have been omitted, though they are implicit in the tales themselves.

The tales deal with a variety of problems: vanity, greed, ingratitude, hypocrisy, envy, superstition, friendship, the relations between the poor and the rich, women's wiles, deceit, in fact all human qualities except sexual love.

Count Lucanor is rich in irony, humor, and its shrewd insight into human nature. Though the themes are varied, the style is always simple, clear, and direct. And the ideals are humanity, loyalty, friendship, religious faith, and common sense.

The fables were inspired by many sources: ancient Oriental tales, Aesop, the *Arabian Nights,* Jewish folklore, historical and legendary incidents of Spain, oral tradition, and from episodes in Don Juan's own life.

Count Lucanor has been widely read and admired since its creation, and many of its tales served as inspiration for some of the world's great writers, such as La Fontaine, Calderón, and Ruiz de Alarcón. Shakespeare's *Taming of the Shrew* is taken from "About a Young Man Who Married a High-Strung Wife." The Archpriest of Hita's "The Fox Who Ate Chickens," contained in his *Libro de Buen Amor* (*The Book of Good Love*), derives from "The Fox Who Pretended to Be Dead."

Count Lucanor is the finest Spanish prose work of the fourteenth century and a forerunner of the modern European novel. The tales selected for this collection are the only English translations in existence, and they appear for the first time for children. They were chosen from the original fifty for their appeal, their variety, and, above all, because they are good stories.

Toby Talbot
February, 1970

DON JUAN MANUEL, a nephew of King Alfonso the Learned, was born in 1281. Active in politics as well as literature, he served as Regent of Castile under Alfonso XI and fought against the Moors. His masterpiece, *The Book of Examples of Count Lucanor and Patronio,* was completed in 1335, over a decade before Boccaccio's *Decameron* with which it is often compared.

TOBY TALBOT was born and raised in New York, but she has always had a pull toward things Spanish. A former education editor of *El Diario de Nueva York,* her translations include *On Love* and *The Origin of Philosophy* by José Ortega y Gasset. She is also the author of several children's books.

ROCCO NEGRI was born in Italy and raised in Argentina. He took art courses there and continued his studies at the Art Students League and the School of Visual Arts upon arriving in New York. Mr. Negri is the illustrator of *Fee, Fi, Fo, Fum* and *Bantu Tales,* and has a number of forthcoming books for which he has done woodcuts.